W9-ADZ-582

APOLLO

APOLLO

RETOLD BY
KATHERINE MILLER

WOODCUTS BY VIVIAN BERGER

1970

Houghton Mifflin Company Boston

Dedicated to the children of P. S. 96

First Printing W

Library of Congress Catalog Card Number 72-105248
Printed in the U.S.A.

CONTENTS

1

THE BIRTH OF APOLLO

LONG, LONG AGO, when the world was young, gods sometimes came down and walked upon the earth. At least that is what people said in the faraway land of Greece. They told many stories about their gods, and about the things they did on earth, among men.

Most of the gods lived on a mountaintop, forever hidden by clouds. But one god lived in a house of golden light, low in the eastern sky, below the edge of the world. His name was Apollo, and he was the most beautiful of all the gods. He was also one of the most powerful. Only the king of the gods, great Zeus his father, was more powerful than he.

Now, the birth of Apollo came about in this way. His mother was a beautiful Titan named Leto. Because she was a Titan, she was immortal, like the gods themselves, and could never die. And Zeus loved her. But the queen of the gods was jealous. She drove Leto away from the gods' mountaintop, and made her wander over the earth, an outcast.

Homeless and unwanted, Leto came at last to a small rocky island. There she was made welcome. And there twins were born, a boy and a girl — children of the great god Zeus. Leto named them Apollo and Artemis.

From the first the children were strong, swift of foot, and more beautiful than any children in all the world of gods or men. To each of them Leto gave a bow and arrows — gold ones for the boy, silver ones for the girl. And she taught them skill in hunting. No god had greater skill. No animal could run too fast for their little arrows. No bird could fly too high. And always the girl's aim was as true as her brother's.

Leto taught the children about the gods, too.

In the beginning, she told them, there were Earth and Heaven. And Earth and Heaven had many children. First came twelve Titans, strong and beautiful. Heaven and Earth were proud of them. But after the Titans came terrible creatures: Giants and one-eyed Cyclopes. Heaven, their father, wished that they had never been born.

Three of the Giants were monsters with fifty heads and a hundred arms. Heaven was afraid of them. So he put them down under the earth and piled a great mountain on top of them.

The Cyclopes were ugly things with one round eye in the middle of their foreheads. Heaven hid them inside the mountain, because he did not like to look on them. There in the mountain they worked at great fires, and there they made lightning and thunderbolts.

Apollo and Artemis loved to hear about all of these

beings. But best of all they loved to hear of the Titans. And Leto loved to tell about them. She told the children of her father, who was a Titan. She told them also of their father's father, who was king of the Titans. His name was Cronus, and he was the most powerful of all the Titans. He was so powerful that he even overcame his father Heaven, and drove him far away from Earth.

In a later time Cronus himself had children, who made war on him. They were the great gods, and Zeus was their leader. But the Titans did not want Zeus to be their king, so they helped Cronus in his fight against his children.

For ten long years there was war between the Titans and the children of Cronus. Finally, Zeus went down into the earth and let loose the Giants. He brought them up into the light to fight beside him. Then he opened the top of the mountain where the Cyclopes were shut. He let out the smoke that burned their eyes, and gave them a sight of the sky. So the Cyclopes gave him their mighty thunderbolts.

Then Zeus took his stand on his mountaintop, with his brothers and sisters around him. From there he hurled the thunderbolts at the Titans. And the Giants took up great rocks to throw.

A hundred rocks at a time the Giants threw with their hundred arms. Even whole hills they lifted up to hurl against the Titans. Thunder crashed, lightning flashed across the sky. Mountains rocked, winds roared, and the cool green sea began to boil.

Zeus hurled his thunderbolts until the sky was full of fire and the whole world shook. Mountains fell into the valleys. The wide seas rose up in great waves and washed over the land. And the noise and roaring shook the very sky.

It was as if sea and earth and sky all crashed together, as god fought god.

In the end, the mighty Titans fell. The children of Cronus drove them deep down under the earth, far deeper than the Giants had been. There in the dark and the mist Zeus chained them to the roots of the mountains.

But not Cronus. For Cronus fled to a land across the sea. There people changed his name to Saturn. And there they did him honor as the father of the gods.

Then Leto told her children how the sons of Cronus divided the world among themselves. One son became God of the Sea. One became God of the Underworld. And one, the strongest of them, became God of the Heavens. That god was great Zeus, their father.

All this Leto taught them on their rocky island.

When Apollo and Artemis were grown, Zeus came down to the earth to see them, and he gave them gifts. To young Apollo he gave a chariot made of bright gold and pulled by four fiery horses. Because he was proud of him, he made Apollo the God of the Sun and gave him powers of healing. He gave Artemis a silver chariot and made her Goddess of the Moon.

From that time, Apollo was ruler of the daytime sky. He warmed the earth and gave it light. And men honored him.

Every day Apollo drove his shining chariot across the sky. How bright it shone! Yet the young god himself, standing in the chariot, shone brightest of all. Men looked up from the earth far below, and their eyes were dazzled. God, chariot, and horses, all seemed to be one shining fiery ball. Each morning men saw the god come up from his home in the east. They saw him climb high in the sky at noon. And they saw him go down into the west at night.

So golden Apollo, the son of Zeus, took his place among the gods.

2

THE BATTLE WITH PYTHON

APOLLO was God of the Sun, but he was not content. All that he had came from his father. He felt he must do something on his own. He must make a place for himself in the world of gods — as a boy must do for himself in the world of men.

Because Apollo gave light to the world, nothing could be hidden from him. His farseeing eyes could see even things that were yet to be. Through this power to know the future he hoped to become the protector of mankind, and to make a name as an Oracle — a wise God of Prophecy.

But there already lived a creature calling itself Oracle.

Now, it had happened long before, in the dim beginnings of time, that the gods became angry with mankind, and sent floods to cover the earth. All living creatures drowned (except one man and one woman).

When the floodwaters went down, the earth was covered with mud and ooze. Then the black mud moved. It bubbled, it boiled. And from its slimy blackness there came a monster of a black snake. Its body was as thick as the body of a man, and longer than the tallest tree is tall. It had an evil forked tongue, and ugly red eyes half hidden by slimy gray-green lids. From head to tail, it was covered with hard black scales made of iron.

Because the snake came from deep in the earth, it knew the secrets of the earth, and had the gift of prophecy.

The monster made its home on the side of a mountain, at a place called Delphi. There it told the future to those who were brave enough to come. Or foolish enough. Because sometimes the snake's words were lying words. Sometimes the advice it gave was evil.

The monster was called Python, the Oracle.

Before Apollo could become the Oracle, he must slay Python. So, with his golden bow and arrows, he came to Delphi.

Above the valley where Python lay there was a cliff of shining rocks, half-hidden now by the great black coils of the snake's body. On that cliff Apollo took his stand. And his golden light filled the valley.

The snake blinked its red eyes in the sudden glare. It hissed a terrible hiss, like a saw cutting through steel. The folds of its body began to coil and twist as it reared its ugly head.

Then Apollo fitted an arrow to the string of his bow. He took aim, and he shot, straight at the monster's head. And his aim was good. There was a ping as metal struck metal. But the arrow glanced off, to fall harmless! So Apollo shot again. Arrow after arrow he shot, as the snake's ugly head rose higher and higher. Finally, the head was almost as high as Apollo was. The red eyes looked into the clear eyes of the god. Steam hissed from the ugly mouth. But no arrow could find a weak spot in those iron scales. The arrows only made the creature angry.

Then the snake coiled its body for attack. Tighter and tighter it drew its coils. Suddenly, like a steel spring let loose, it hurled itself through the air at the young god.

When Apollo saw the thing coming, he jumped to one side. But quick as he was, the snake was quicker. Its iron head struck him with the force of a thunderbolt and threw him to the ground. His head hit a stone.

The god lay there dazed. He felt the snake draw its iron coils around him. He felt the monster's body squeezing the breath from him. He saw the ugly head high above him. Its evil red eyes glared down at him. Then he saw the head start toward him, its forked tongue darting.

With the last of his strength, Apollo fitted one more arrow to the string of his bow and aimed at one of those red eyes. From where he lay, held by the snake's coils, the eye seemed to be the barest slit. But he knew it was his only hope.

So he drew the bow as best he could, and sent the arrow flying. And, wonder of wonders, he saw the

arrow go in! He had found the only soft spot in all the Python's body.

The snake hissed its terrible hiss again. Its coils relaxed for a moment. And Apollo pulled himself free. Then the black body began to twist and thrash. The tail lashed at the god. It almost pushed him off the cliff. Apollo dropped his bow and jumped onto the monster's back. With one arm around Python's neck he held tight, as the creature thrashed from side to side. With his other hand he drove the arrow deeper and deeper into the snake's head. Black blood splashed on the rocks and on Apollo. Hiss after hiss filled the air. The snake's wild thrashing even made the mountain shake.

Then, at last, Apollo felt the creature shudder. Slowly its head sank to the ground. Its long body relaxed. There was one last hiss, like a sigh, and Python was dead.

By this great deed, Apollo became Oracle — the Oracle of Delphi.

There, below the cliff of shining rocks, men made a temple for the god. There, in their need, they came to ask his help. And through the priests of the temple, Apollo spoke to them. He gave advice for those who needed advice, comfort for those who needed comfort, warning for those who needed warning.

And always the words of Apollo were wise and just — so different from the words that Python had spoken, with its evil forked tongue.

HOW APOLLO WAS TRICKED

APOLLO, the God of the Sun, had a herd of snow-white cattle: cows, and bulls, and playful calves. How pretty they looked in the blue meadow of the sky, and how proud he was of them.

But —

Apollo had a young half brother named Hermes. From the day Hermes was born he was strong and full of mischief. When he was only a few hours old, he jumped out of his cradle and ran away. He wanted to look at the wonderful new world he lived in.

What a lot of things he found to have fun with. There were sand and mud to walk through with bare feet, water to splash, birds and butterflies to chase. There were wiggly snakes and toads and lizards, sticks to dig with, stones to throw. A wonderful world!

Then Hermes saw a thing like a big brown stone lying on the ground. When he picked it up, he found that it was hollow like a bowl. And it shone like gold when he looked at the sunlight through it. It was the shell of a tortoise. What fun Hermes had with it! It was a hat; it was a boat. He stretched a piece of skin across it and it was a drum, rat-a-tat-tat!

Then he had another idea. He made two holes in one end of the shell and put sticks in the holes — a frame of sticks that looked like an H with long legs. He stretched strings from end to end of his toy, and plucked the strings, and found that it made pretty music. Hermes called the toy a lyre. And that lyre was the grandfather of all the world's guitars.

But soon Hermes grew tired of his plaything. So he hung it over his shoulder and went on.

Late in the day, as the sun was going down, he came to a green meadow on a mountainside. There he found a herd of white cattle, the cattle of his half brother Apollo. They had just come from their meadow in the sky to rest for the night there on the mountainside.

Hermes scampered around among the animals, chasing the cows, racing with the calves, and teasing the bulls. These were playthings a boy would not grow tired of. How he wished that they were his, to play with every day.

No sooner wished, than planned. The bad little boy decided to steal them! He would take them across a rocky ridge and hide them in a valley on the other side. But he must leave no telltale tracks in the meadow to show which way they had gone. So he picked up a stick and began to race from side to side, trying to make the animals turn around and back away to the rocky ridge. And, what is more, he did it!

What a sight it was — a herd of fifty snow-white cattle, going backward across the meadow, mooing and bellowing, with a baby boy running around among them waving a little stick. And laughing with glee.

When they came to a sandy place, Hermes was stopped for a moment, but only for a moment. He knew his own baby footprints would show in the sand, so he cut branches from a tree and tied them to his feet. Then, walking on leaves, he crossed the sand and left never a footprint.

Soon the cattle came to the rocky ridge. They crossed it, and were gone, down the other side. And, wonder of wonders, their tracks made it look as if they had come *from* the ridge instead of going *to* it.

When Apollo came for his cattle the next day, the meadow was empty, except for one lonely old bull with twisted horns that had somehow been left behind. Apollo saw lots of tracks coming *to* the meadow, but no tracks leading away from it. It was as if the cattle had simply disappeared from the middle of the meadow.

Now, Apollo had eyes that saw more than other eyes could see. As soon as he put his mind to it, he knew that his bad baby brother had stolen the cattle. But where did he hide them? And how did he get them out of the meadow? Apollo knew there was a trick to it. But he did not know what the trick was. So he went to look for Hermes.

He found him lying in his little cradle, kicking his baby feet in the air. Hermes knew very well who Apollo was. He knew also that trouble was coming. So he gurgled a baby song, and made pretty plinking sounds on his new toy.

"Good morning," said Apollo. "I am your big brother."

"Lyre!" gurgled the baby, and held out his toy in his fat little hand.

Apollo was annoyed. "Liar?" he said. "Now listen to me, baby brother. I am here to find out what you have done with my cattle."

"Lyre," the baby gurgled again, and plucked the strings, pling-pling, plang.

"Don't make me angry," said the god, already angry. "I know that you know where my cattle are hidden."

"Lyre!" And this time the gurgle was almost a giggle. The bad little boy was having fun.

"Stop calling me liar!" shouted Apollo. He took the baby up in both hands and stood him on his two baby feet.

"Now, march!" he ordered. "Show me where my cattle are, or I will put you over my knee and spank you!"

Then Hermes knew he had better do as his big brother told him. So off he scampered. At the meadow he turned to face Apollo. With a grin he began to run away backward toward the rocky ridge. Then Apollo saw what the trick was, and he laughed. His anger began to go. What a smart one his baby brother was.

Soon they came to the valley. And there, under the trees, were the cattle, safe and sound. The last of Apollo's anger left him.

"It seems you took good care of them," he said. "And a good thing, too. But why did you keep calling me liar?"

"I didn't call you liar," said the boy, with mischief in his eyes. "I was showing you my toy." He held it up and ran his fingers across the strings. "See. This is a lyre. L – y – r – e, lyre."

Apollo laughed again. "Well, baby brother, you have tricked me twice," he said. "But I like your toy. Give it to me and I will forgive you for stealing my cattle. I'll even let you take care of them for me, since you like them so much. But — NO MORE TRICKS!" he said sternly.

So Hermes gave Apollo the lyre. When the golden god touched the strings, music came from them such as the world had never heard. It was as if the lyre had been waiting for just his touch.

Thus Apollo, God of the Sun, of Healing, and of Prophecy, became also the God of Music and of Poetry.

And what of Hermes? Was he sorry for what he had done? Not a bit. He was only sorry he had been found out. Yet he could be glad that Apollo let him stay with his pretty pets.

Thus Hermes took his place as God of Herdsmen and — as one might guess — God of Thieves. Zeus, his father, made him also the messenger of the gods, and gave him magic sandals with silver wings on them. With them Hermes was able to fly through the air, like the birds and butterflies he had chased on that first wonderful day of his life.

Across the sea people changed his name to Mercury, a name that means "Quicksilver." And that is just what he was most like, with his swift silver sandals — quicksilver.

4

APOLLO AND HERCULES

APOLLO WAS PROUD of his powers. He would let no one be his equal. Not even the strongest man in the world.

That man was a hero named Hercules. Zeus was his father, too, and so Apollo was his half brother. But Hercules was only half god, because his mother was a mortal.

Hercules was a giant of a man. He was so strong that, on the day he was born, he killed two great snakes, with his bare baby hands. One thing kept him from being the greatest hero the world has ever known. That was his temper. He had a temper that would flare up suddenly for the smallest thing. When it did, he was like a madman.

One time his temper got him in trouble with Apollo.

It happened that there was a king who had a beautiful daughter. Hercules wanted to marry her. But because of his terrible temper, the king did not want the girl to marry Hercules. So he set up a contest: the king promised to give the girl to anyone who could defeat himself and his sons in a contest with bow and arrows.

Now, bow and arrows were not what Hercules was best at, as the king knew very well. But, even so,

Hercules was willing to try his luck. And, to the king's horror, he won!

Then the king went back on his promise. He said that the winning arrow did not belong to Hercules at all. Instead, he said that the arrow was his own, and his three younger sons all took his side. Only the oldest son, whose name was Iphitus, spoke up for Hercules. Iphitus thought that his father was not being fair. He said everyone knew that the winning arrow belonged to Hercules, and he should have what he had won.

But nothing could change the king's mind. In the end, Hercules had to go away, angry but empty-handed.

Not long after this, some of the king's horses were stolen. The thief was a young fellow named Autolycus, who was always up to some kind of mischief, just like Hermes, the god he worshiped. Autolycus would steal anything, whether he wanted it or not, just like Hermes. So, when he saw the chance, he ran away with twelve of the king's prize horses. But he had no use for them, and he sold them to Hercules.

They were beautiful horses, with long silky manes. Hercules was proud of them. He rode them, he raced them, he talked about them far and wide. Very soon the king knew who had his horses. He thought that Hercules had stolen them, in revenge. And he sent Iphitus to try to get them back.

Hercules was glad to see Iphitus. He gave him food and wine, and took him to see his horses. But when Iphitus asked if he had stolen them from the king, a sudden wild anger came over Hercules. This was too much to bear! With an angry roar, he picked Iphitus up and shook him. Then, holding him by one arm, like a toy, he climbed up onto the wall of the city. From there he hurled the poor boy down to the ground, with all his might.

Then his anger left him, as suddenly as it had come. He looked down. Below him he saw the body of his friend, lying at the foot of the wall, like a broken rag doll. He leaped down to it and lifted it from the stones. But it was too late. Iphitus was dead.

Hercules was filled with horror at what he had done. He wept and cursed and pulled his hair. Then he went to the Oracle at Delphi to ask Apollo what he must do to pay for the murder of his friend.

In the temple Hercules found the priestess of Apollo seated on a beautiful seat. It was made all of gold, with three legs like twisted golden snakes. Because it had three legs, the seat was called the Tripod.

Hercules stood before the priestess and asked her to tell him what he should do. She looked up at him standing over her, his head unbowed, and she said nothing.

"Speak to me, old woman," he demanded. "What does Apollo say?" Still the priestess only looked at him.

Hercules was beginning to be angry. "I am Hercules," he cried. "I demand that you speak!"

For a third time he got no answer.

Then madness came over Hercules again. But this time it was a madness such as he had never felt before. Everything he saw seemed to turn red. The temple seemed filled with a red mist. The candles seemed to burn with red flames; they dripped drops that looked like drops of red blood. The old priestess, sitting before him in the red light, looked like a grinning witch. And the snakes that were the legs of the Tripod seemed to be alive, coiling and hissing.

In his madness Hercules rushed at the old woman. He pushed her from the Tripod and picked it up.

"There is no Oracle here!" he shouted. Holding the Tripod high, he ran out of the temple. "I have the Tripod now! I will be the Oracle! Down with Apollo!"

At those words there was a flash of golden light. Apollo himself stood before Hercules.

"Give me my Tripod," said the god sternly.

"No!" Hercules shouted, leaping away from him. "You are no Oracle!"

"Thief! Put down my Tripod!"

"No! No! No!" Hercules shouted in his madness. "I will be the Oracle!" And he held the Tripod close.

Apollo raised his bow. "Drop the Tripod!" he cried in a voice like thunder.

Then Hercules swung the heavy Tripod, to throw it straight at Apollo's head. And Apollo aimed his arrow right between Hercules's eyes. There was death in the hearts of both of them, as they faced each other, hero against god.

But Zeus was watching his two angry sons. At the moment that Apollo shot his deadly arrow and Hercules sent the Tripod flying through the air, Zeus hurled his thunderbolt. He threw a ball of fire between the god and the hero, between the arrow and the Tripod.

The earth shook and opened up between the brothers, as the thunderbolt struck. Both Apollo and Hercules were thrown to the ground. And the arrow and the Tripod both missed their marks.

When their heads cleared, Apollo and Hercules got to their feet. All their anger was gone. They reached out and took hands, brother to brother.

"Why would you not answer me?" Hercules asked.

"Why did you demand an answer?" asked Apollo.

Hercules fell to his knees before the god. He bowed his head and begged to know what he must do to pay for his friend's murder.

And then Apollo answered him. He told him that he must let himself be sold to work as a slave for three years, and that he must give all the money to the king whose son he had killed.

And Hercules did as Apollo said.

ASSES' EARS

THE GODS of the Greeks were in many ways not very godlike. Of course, they were brave and beautiful as only gods can be. And they had powers that only gods have. But they also had all the faults that mortals have. There were even times when they were more like bad-tempered children than like grown-up men and women.

Of all the gods, Apollo was one of the most godlike, yet even he sometimes had fits of bad temper. As will be seen.

There was a woodland god named Pan, a god of herds. He was a strange creature, half man, half goat, with little horns growing from his man's head. With the other woodland gods, and nymphs (lovely beings that were almost goddesses), Pan lived a carefree life in the high hills. He spent his days among his sheep and goats, playing his pipes.

Pan was famous for his pipes. He had made them out of a handful of reeds from the river. When he blew across the reeds he filled the woods with music. With his gay pipings Pan was the center of the sports and games of the woodland gods and nymphs.

There was a mortal living in Pan's woodlands, too. He was a king named Midas. This was the same Midas who had wished for the golden touch. It was a foolish wish, as the god who granted it knew. And the poor king almost starved to death because of it. Everything he touched, even every crumb of bread and every drop of water, turned to pure gold.

When the golden touch was finally taken away, the king had had enough of riches. He left his palace and went to live a simple life in the woods and fields. There he heard Pan's woodland piping, and said it was the most beautiful music in all the world.

So Pan began to think his music might be as good as that of Apollo, the God of Music — or even better. In his pride he dared Apollo to meet him in a contest.

"If my music is better than yours," he said, "then I will be God of Music."

"So be it," said Apollo, but he was annoyed with this upstart goat-god.

"Shall I arrange the contest and find a judge?" asked Pan.

"So be it," said Apollo. He would let Pan have every advantage, and would still put him in his place!

Pan arranged the contest as he wished. It would be on the mountainside where he lived, with all his woodland friends looking on. King Midas would be there too. The judge would be old Timolus, god of the mountain.

On the high hillside the goat-god Pan, with his reed pipes, met golden Apollo, with his lyre. Between them sat old Timolus. And he looked like the mountain he

was god of. Around his stately head, with its ice-blue hair, there was a crown of oak trees. His great brown feet were placed firmly before him, immovable as the mountain itself. At the feet of these three sat the woodland gods and nymphs.

But Midas took a seat in the highest place, beside Timolus — like a judge himself! Foolish Midas. He had been cured of his golden touch, but not even a god could cure him of his foolishness.

Pan put his pipes to his lips and began to play. He played as he had never played before — like millions of birds, like sunlight on the river, like waterfalls, and wind in the trees. All of his love for his woodlands was in the music he played. It filled the hearts of the nymphs and gods with a wild wonderful joy. Apollo, too, knew that here was music worth the hearing.

But then Apollo touched the strings of his lyre, and the woodlands seemed to melt away. The listeners felt themselves lifted to the high heavens, where Apollo drove his shining chariot. From there they saw the earth below them, with its green lands in wide blue seas, looking small and beautiful. They saw the heavens around the earth, with the shining stars and the sun and the moon.

As they watched, it seemed that time ran faster. They saw dark spread over the earth as night came, then day, and night, and day again — and winter and spring, and summer again. And then they knew that this was the way Apollo saw the earth — a small blue ball for the gods to cherish.

When Apollo stopped, all the listeners knew that this was the God of Music who played. And they bowed their heads in honor of him.

All but Midas.

Foolish Midas said he liked the pipes of Pan much better. All he heard from the lyre, he said, was silly plinking.

Then Apollo forgave Pan for his daring. He turned all his bad temper on Midas.

"Donkey!" he cried. "Jackass! May the ears you hear with look like what they are!" And he was gone.

Then all those left on the hillside began to laugh! They held their sides and rolled on the grass with laughter. They laughed until tears ran down their faces.

All but Midas.

He did not even see the joke. He only felt his ears itching and twitching. He put his hands up to scratch them — and he found that they were long and hairy! Just like the ears of the jackass that the god had called him!

So Midas fled, never to come there again. Home he fled, and hid himself. He said he was sick. And he was.

He hid for as long as he could. But even a sick king must eat. When Midas finally showed himself, he was wearing a bright silk scarf around his head to hide his ears.

But not even a king can stop his hair from growing. And no barber can cut the hair of a man who is wearing a hat. So King Midas's barber learned the terrible secret. But — he learned it on pain of death if ever he told it.

That secret almost drove the poor barber crazy. How

he longed to tell it. What good is a secret that can't be told? How he ached to tell it! Yet he feared for his life if he did. The poor man lived in terror that he might blurt it out, or talk in his sleep.

If only he could tell the secret just once, he thought, he could find peace.

Finally, the barber went, in the dark of night, far out into a meadow by the river. There he dug a deep hole. Then he climbed down into the hole — and there he whispered his terrible secret. After that he filled the hole and went home. At last, he could sleep soundly.

In time, reeds grew up in the soft earth over the hole. When the wind blew across the reeds, they whispered among themselves the secret that the barber told: "King Midas has asses' ears," they said. "King Midas has asses' ears."

A man, passing the bed of reeds, heard the whispering. At first he could not believe his own ears. Then he remembered the scarf that the king always wore, and he knew that what he heard was true. How he laughed! His king had the ears of a donkey! With glee he ran to spread the news. Soon everyone was laughing at the king and the secret of his foolish asses' ears — the secret that the reeds had whispered.

And still they whisper it, to this day. Whenever the wind blows over reeds by a river you can hear them whispering about foolish King Midas, who stirred the anger of Apollo: "King Midas has asses' ears — Midas has asses' ears — asses' ears — Midas has . . ."

ON A DOLPHIN'S BACK

THOSE WHO HONORED APOLLO knew him to be a kind and loving god, as the story that follows will show.

There was once a singer named Arion. He was a mortal, not a god, but his skill was almost godlike. With all his heart he worshiped Apollo, the God of Music.

Arion went to many lands singing his songs and playing his lyre. He sang for all who wanted to hear him, for poor men as well as for kings. All gave him gifts. The poor gave copper pennies. The rich gave gold and beautiful robes for him to wear when he sang. So Arion became rich and famous.

At last, a time came when he longed to see his home again. He found a ship that was going to Greece and went on board, carrying his gold in a leather bag. Under a clear sky the ship set sail.

At first all went well. Then one of the sailors began to wonder about the bag that Arion carried. He told the other sailors he had heard the sound of clinking from the bag. If it were full of gold, he said, it would make them all rich. The sailors decided to steal the bag.

It would not be easy. Arion kept the bag always with him. He even slept with his head on it at night. So the sailors watched and planned and waited. They wanted to steal it in such a way that Arion would think it had fallen into the sea.

Soon a day came when clouds covered the sky. Winds blew. Waves tossed the ship. At night the clouds hid the light of the moon, so all was dark. It was what the sailors had been waiting for.

"Tonight is the night," they whispered to each other.

When Arion was asleep, they came to where he lay. They stood around him in the dark, waiting for a large wave to rock the ship. Their plan was this: when the wave came, one of them would drag the bag from under Arion's head, while a second sailor would splash water on the deck beside Arion. Thus it would seem that the wave had washed the bag away.

But the wave, when it came, was much bigger than they thought it would be. The sailor stumbled as he threw the water, and it splashed in Arion's face and woke him up. At that very moment moonlight flashed through a hole in the clouds. It lighted the sailors standing around him. He saw them clearly. One of them was holding his bag of gold.

Arion jumped to his feet, crying, "Thieves! Thieves! Help me, captain!"

But the captain was himself one of the thieves. There was no one to help. Instead, the sailors took hold of Arion with their rough hands. Now that he had seen them, they would have to kill him.

Arion knew he was helpless. Even if he got loose, there was nowhere to run. So he watched calmly as the sailors divided his gold among themselves, and drew lots for his beautiful robes. He even listened calmly as they planned his death. They would throw him into the sea, they decided.

But then one of the sailors picked up Arion's lyre from where it lay on the deck. Suddenly he was wild with anger.

"Do not touch my lyre!" he shouted, trying to get free. "Not with your rough hands!"

The sailor laughed an ugly laugh. "You won't be needing it," he said. "Not where you're going."

"Then let me hold it one more time before I die," Arion begged. "Let me hold it just once more, and I will play for you."

"That is fair," said the captain. "Give it to him. I would like to hear our great singer."

So the sailor gave Arion back his lyre. The captain even gave him a robe to sing in. It was one that Arion had worn when he sang before kings.

"But don't think that your singing will make us change our minds," the captain said. The sailors laughed again.

Standing high at one end of the boat, Arion began to play and sing. The song he sang was in honor of Apollo, the god he had worshiped all his life. Never had he sung more beautifully.

As he sang, the clouds began to blow away. Low in the eastern sky was a golden light. Night was almost over.

At the moment that Arion's song ended, a golden ball rose into the sky. It was the sun's chariot. The bright light of it shone full on Arion standing before the sailors. It flashed from the golden lyre in his hand. And Arion knew that Apollo had heard his song. He could die now, happy that his god had smiled on him.

Before the sailors could stop him, Arion jumped into the sea, still holding his lyre in his hand and wearing the beautiful robe.

Down he went, deep into the dark sea. Down and down.

But Arion was not alone in the cold black water. Following him down, into the deep, was a great gray dolphin. Swiftly it raced after him. Swiftly it got under him. Swiftly it pushed him up, out of the sea, to light and air again.

With Arion on his back, the dolphin leaped out of the waves. He leaped up into the golden morning sunlight. The rays of the sun flashed on his shining skin.

Then Arion knew that Apollo had sent the dolphin to save him.

Riding on the dolphin's back, he came safely to land. There he told his story of the sailors and of the dolphin. But no one would believe him. Even his friends laughed at his wild tale of riding on the back of a fish!

"What imagination these poets have," said one.

"If he was drowning, it must have been wine he was drowning in!" said another, and they all laughed.

But soon the ship itself came in. The sailors all had much gold to spend, and they told of leaving Arion safe and sound in Italy. Arion's friends began to wonder. So they brought him to the sailors.

When the sailors saw him, their faces turned white with fear.

"It is a ghost!" the captain cried, and tried to run.

"How can I be a ghost, if you left me safe in Italy?" Arion asked.

Then the sailors confessed, and gave back the gold that they had stolen.

Arion and his friends gave thanks to Apollo for what he had done. In order that men would never forget how the god had saved him, Arion had a statue made and gave it to the temple in honor of Apollo. It was a statue of a man riding on the back of a dolphin.

7

WREATH OF LAUREL

THERE ARE MANY STORIES about Apollo and those he loved, or who loved him. Two of his loves were immortal. They live on, even today.

One of those who loved Apollo was a water nymph named Clytie.

She thought he was the most beautiful being in heaven or on earth. Day after day she stood with her lovely face lifted up to the heavens, watching him as he moved across the sky. Night after night she stood, too, her face turned to the east, waiting for him to appear. She gave no thought to anything but her golden god. She ate no food. She drank only dew, and her own salt tears.

But Apollo could find no love in his heart for Clytie. He felt only pity, as he saw the pretty thing pining away. At last, in kindness, he changed her into a flower, tall and straight and beautiful. Thus she could stand and watch him always, fed by the earth, watered by the rain, and warmed by the god she loved. And because Apollo was touched by her love, he gave her great golden petals, like the rays of his own golden crown.

So still she stands as she did in life. And still each day she turns her face to follow him — this flower that bears his name, the golden sunflower.

There were also those whom Apollo loved, himself.

His first and greatest love was for a nymph named Daphne. This is their story.

Apollo was proud of his skill with bow and arrow. And he was right to be proud, for did he not slay the terrible Python? But there was another god whose bow and arrows were famous, too. He was a handsome boy named Eros — sometimes called Cupid. With his little wings and golden bow, Eros was helper to his mother, the Goddess of Love.

One day Apollo came upon Eros playing with his little bow and arrows. The boy was shooting at apples and falling leaves. When Apollo saw him, he laughed at him.

will always be a hunter, like Artemis. And like her, I will never marry."

So Apollo cursed his own sister, the virgin goddess of the cold silver moon, for stealing his loved one from him.

Finally, he grew tired of begging. He could wait no longer. This time, when Daphne fled, Apollo followed, mad with love. How beautiful she was as she ran, he thought. How beautiful her bare arms were, and her face, her slender body, her shining hair.

Loving the sight of her running, Apollo matched his steps to hers. How swift she was. And her strong brown feet were sure on the woodland path. Apollo knew she would be a mate fit for a god.

Suddenly he was wild to hold her in his arms. I must, he thought, now — this instant! And he began to run faster.

Daphne looked back. She saw the god coming, and was filled with fear. Down the hill she fled toward her father's river, shining in the valley. She ran like the wind, and her bare brown legs were strong and lovely.

But her swift flight was not swift enough. Apollo, with his young god's strength, was soon close behind her. His reaching fingers could almost touch the ends of her flying hair. Then Daphne knew she could not reach the river in time. In despair, she cried out to her father for help. And he heard her cry.

At the moment that Apollo threw his arms around the frightened thing, she felt her flying feet rooted to the ground. She felt her body closed in something rough and hard. She felt her arms become stiff.

And there, on the bank of the river, stood a tree of dark green laurel, its leaves shining in the sunlight.

In place of Daphne's body, Apollo was holding in his arms the trembling trunk of the tree. Daphne's arms were now branches. Her head was a treetop, and her hair had changed to leaves. Their rustling in the wind was like a sigh as the god held her.

For a moment more the pounding heart beat on, inside the rough bark. Then it was still, forever.

Saddened by his loss, Apollo took branches of the laurel and twisted them into a crown to wear around his head.

"This way, at least, I can have her always with me," he said. "And because my love will never die, let the leaves of the laurel be ever green."

And so they are, always green and shining, under summer sun or winter snow, to this very day.

8

THE HORSES OF THE SUN

AS GODS DID in those long-ago days, Apollo sometimes took the form of a man and came down to walk on the earth as a man. There, as a man, he met and loved a woman who was mortal. And they had a son, a beautiful boy named Phaethon.

Phaethon grew up on the earth with his mother. But she told him of his father. Each day the boy watched the Sun God drive his golden chariot across the heavens, and he was proud. He longed for the world to know that this golden god was his father.

When Phaethon had grown to be a young man, he went to live with his father in the heavens. Apollo was proud of his son. In his joy at having him with him, he promised to grant the boy any wish.

Phaethon was young and daring. Many times he had watched his father drive his fiery horses on the trip across the sky. Always he had wished he were driving them himself. So that was what he asked — to drive the chariot of the sun across the heavens, just one time.

Then Apollo was sorry he had promised. He begged Phaethon to make some other wish.

"None but a god can drive the horses of the sun," he told the boy.

"I am your son," Phaethon said, "the son of a god!"

"But your mother was a mortal. You are only half god, my son."

"Yet I want to drive the fiery horses! I want to climb the sky!"

"The horses are wild — too strong for you to hold."

"I will drive them! I will!" cried the boy, and he leaped into the chariot.

Already the great doors of the stable were open. Already the time had come for the sun to be in the sky. The horses were pawing the ground. Fire flamed from their nostrils. They were ready to be off. Before Apollo could say more, Phaethon took the reins in his hand, and the horses leaped into the sky.

What a climb! Up, up, up went the horses — so fast and so high that it took Phaethon's breath away. But his heart was filled with wild joy. Higher than the highest birds the horses went, even higher than the clouds!

Then Phaethon looked down at the earth far below. He saw the light moving across the land, as day spread over the world. And he was proud.

"People will see me driving the horses of the sun. They will know that I, Phaethon, am the son of the Sun God! They will thank me for bringing them warmth and light."

How strong he felt, how full of joy — and how free, with the whole wide sky around him.

But the horses felt that the hands on the reins were different hands. They knew they were not as strong as the ones they were used to. They tossed their heads. They reared and kicked. They liked the feel of fighting hands too weak to hold them.

They turned away from the steep path up to the top of the heavens, and began to race down the sky. Fast and faster they went, and the chariot was dashed from side to side. But how easy it was for the horses, much easier than the hard climb up. So down they plunged, with their bright manes flowing in the wind like flames.

Phaethon pulled on the reins with all his strength. He must get the horses back to the path up the sky! He must! He pulled until his arms ached. He pulled until the sweat ran down his face. He pulled until his eyes were full of tears.

But all his strength was not enough.

The fiery horses of the sun plunged on, down and down, nearer and nearer to the earth. They came so near that the earth began to burn. Trees and grass and houses burned. Rivers and lakes turned into steam. People cried out in terror.

Zeus, the king of the gods, heard the cries of the people. From his home on the mountaintop he looked and saw the world in flames. He saw the chariot of the sun plunging ever nearer to the earth. He knew he must do something to save the earth. And quickly.

So he hurled his mighty thunderbolt at young Phaethon.

The boy fell from the chariot. Like a falling star, he fell — down, down, into the deep of the sea.

Then the horses were afraid and slowed their wild dash. They stopped their plunge to the earth and turned to find once more the path they knew. In the end, they made their way to the gates of night in the west of the world. At last the terrible day was over.

But Phaethon was dead, in the sea.

There he was found by gentle river nymphs. They took him up from the sea, and made a grave for him on the shore of the sea. Over him, his sisters shed golden tears. The night winds sang sad songs. And Apollo himself came down to mourn for his son.

On his grave they put these words:

Here lies young Phaethon,
Son of the Sun God.
He dared to do deeds that gods do
And died for his daring.

9

THE BABY IN THE BASKET

THE WAYS OF THE GODS are not the ways of mortals. And gods cannot be judged by the laws of men. All men know that. Yet, even so, Apollo did one deed that no man could forgive.

Perhaps he did it in his wild sorrow for his dead son. Perhaps it was in his pride as one of the great gods. Who can say? But it was not worthy of a god.

One day Apollo was hunting on a mountainside. Below him, in a field of yellow flowers, he saw a lovely young girl. Her father was King of Athens, and her name was Creusa.

The moment Apollo saw the girl, he wanted her. So he took her. Before she knew what was happening, he picked her up and took her into a cave in the mountainside.

Creusa was frightened. She screamed; she bit at the god's arms; she scratched at his face; she pulled his shining hair. But Apollo only laughed and held her tighter. In the cool dimness of the cave he put her down on a bed of leaves. And there, in spite of her cries, he raped her. Then he left her.

How she hated Apollo! Her body ached. Her dress was torn. Her face was streaked with tears. Hurt and frightened, the poor girl made her way home.

But worse was yet to come.

Soon Creusa knew that she was going to have a child. For months she lived in terror that her father would find out about the baby. If he did, what could she say? Who would believe that the baby was the child of a god? Who would believe that a god would do what Apollo had done? People would say that she had made the story up to hide her shame. Her father might even put her to death. So she told no one. And all the time she kept hoping that Apollo would come back to tell the world that the baby was his. But he never came.

In the end, when she knew it was time for the baby to be born, Creusa went back, alone, to the same dim cave where Apollo had taken her. There a son was born. And there she left the baby.

She wrapped the little thing in a cloth woven by her own hands, and put him in a basket. But as she turned to go away, the baby reached out its little hand to her. Weeping, she took a golden necklace from her own neck and put it in the tiny fist. Then she left the little thing, all alone. Surely, she thought, Apollo would claim his child at last. Surely he would not let his own son die.

But still no word came from the god. So Creusa went back, once more, to the cave.

To her horror, the baby was gone! Even the basket was gone, and the cloth, and the necklace.

She looked everywhere. There was no footprint but her own; so no one had been there. There was no blood; so wild animals had not torn the child. What had happened? Had an eagle taken the baby away, as food for its young? There was no way to know. And she wept for her lost child.

But it was not an eagle.

When Apollo saw the baby left alone in the cave, he sent his young brother Hermes to get the child. On winged feet, Hermes sped through the air. He picked the baby up, basket and all, and took it to the temple of the Oracle at Delphi. There he left it on the steps of the temple — Apollo's temple. And there an old priestess found the baby, and cared for him, like a mother. So the boy grew up at the temple, as a servant to the god Apollo, his own father — although no one knew it.

In time, Creusa was married. When her father died, she became Queen of Athens. But she was not happy. For no children came to her and her husband.

Finally, after many years, her husband asked her to go with him to the Oracle.

"We must ask Apollo for children, to rule Athens after we are gone," he said.

"No!" cried Creusa. "Not Apollo!"

"Why not?" her husband asked.

But she could not tell him why. So, at last, she went with him.

When they came to the temple, Creusa waited outside and let her husband go in alone. A beautiful boy was sweeping the steps of the temple. He was dressed in a robe like those the priests wore, and his golden hair shone in the morning sunlight. Creusa's heart was moved at the sight of the boy.

"Who are you?" she asked him.

"I am called Ion," he said, "and I serve Apollo."

"But who is your mother?" she asked.

"I do not know," the boy said. "I was found on these steps when I was a baby. The priestess is the only mother I have ever known. This temple is my only home."

"Poor boy. You have no mother, and I have no child." Tears of longing filled Creusa's eyes.

Before she could say more, the doors of the temple opened and her husband came out. He looked all about him. Then his eyes fell on Ion. With a joyful smile he rushed down the steps and threw his arms around the boy.

"My son!" he said.

The boy pulled away from him. "What do you mean, old man? Are you mad?" he asked.

"No, I am not mad. The Oracle has spoken. Apollo said that the one I met as I came from the temple would be my son."

"Your own son, or a gift?" Creusa asked.

"My own and a gift."

"And you are truly my father?" asked the boy.

"Yes, my son. I am truly your father."

"But what of me?" Creusa wanted to know. "Am I to have no children? What did the god say of me?"

"He said nothing. Not a word."

Hot tears of anger filled her eyes. "So Apollo has given you a son! But do not think that your bastard will ever be King of Athens!" she cried. "He is not of the royal line. And I will not have it!"

"It is Apollo's will."

"Do not speak to me of Apollo! Apollo is evil!"

At that word, a hush of fear fell on everyone there. Surely the god would strike Creusa dead, they thought. For a long moment they waited. But nothing happened.

"Yes, Apollo is evil," she said again. "I will be silent no longer."

Then, at last, she told the story of how Apollo had betrayed her, and of the baby she had left to die in the cave.

"Now," she ended, "Apollo would betray me once more. He would put a stranger on the throne of Athens. But I will not have it!"

Suddenly a knife flashed in her hand. She rushed at Ion.

But the boy was quick. He caught her arm in his strong young hand, and the knife fell to the ground.

"Murderer!" he shouted.

At that moment the old priestess came to the door of the temple.

"My children!" she said. "Put away your anger! You must be friends."

Then she handed a little basket to Ion. "Here, my son. Apollo has told me to give you this. I have kept it hidden all the years since first I found you in it, here on these steps. Now may it help you to find your mother."

At sight of the basket, Creusa began to tremble. She was almost unable to believe what she saw.

"I — I am his mother!" she whispered.

"But you tried to kill me," said the boy.

"I did not know," she said, and her face was white. "I did not know."

Then, to show that what she said was true, Creusa told them what was in the basket. She told of the cloth that she had wrapped the baby in, so long ago. She told how she had woven the cloth with her own girlish hands. She told of the golden necklace that she had put in the baby's little fist. And they found that it was all just as she said.

"But why did Apollo give the boy to my husband?" she asked the old priestess.

"It was his way of giving him back to you, and giving him an earthly father at the same time," the priestess said. "It was the god's way of giving the boy his proper place in the world."

So, at long last, Apollo brought happiness to Creusa. But she knew that he did it only because it was the one sure way he could save the life of his son.

Thus it was that Apollo put his own son on the throne of Athens.

ONE-EYES

IN LATER TIMES Apollo had other sons. Two of them came to be worshiped almost like gods. Both were mortal, yet both were more than mortal, for Apollo was their father, and he gave to them some of his own great powers.

One son was Orpheus. Apollo gave him the gift of music, and Orpheus became the greatest singer the world has ever known. The music he made was so beautiful that even wild animals and trees and rivers would come to listen. He was a true son of the God of Music.

Another son was named Asclepius. To him Apollo gave the gift of healing. From near and far the sick came to him, and those wounded in battle. Always he took away their pain and made them well again.

But in the end Asclepius used his gift in a way that made Zeus angry. For, in the end, he dared to do what only a god may do. He dared to bring a dead man back to life.

So Zeus hurled his thunderbolt at Asclepius and struck him down.

Then Apollo was wild with sorrow and anger. Two of his sons dead! Both by thunderbolts from the hand of Zeus. Apollo cursed Zeus, and longed for revenge.

But not even Apollo dared take revenge on Zeus. Instead, he turned his anger on the workmen who made the thunderbolts. They were the Cyclopes, those creatures with one round eye in the middle of their foreheads.

Apollo came to the mountain where the Cyclopes worked. He stood on the rim of the opening in the top of the mountain and looked down into the fiery heart of it. There, in the red light of roaring fires, he saw three great black shapes moving. He saw flames lick at the powerful arms of the creatures as they lifted white-hot iron from the fire. He saw those arms swing great hammers. He heard the clang of metal on metal as the Cyclopes made the thunderbolts for Zeus.

As he looked down at them, Apollo felt his anger growing. He fitted an arrow to the string of his bow and took aim. But before he let the arrow go, he called to them by name.

"Bright! Thunderous! Lightener!" he called. "Hear me, O Cyclopes!"

The three workmen looked up. Their great round eyes glared at Apollo far above them, shining against the blue sky.

"With your thunderbolts Zeus has slain my sons.

So, die, you murderers! Die!" Apollo shouted. "Your lives for the lives of my sons!" And he sent his arrow flying, into the heart of Thunderous.

Before the Cyclopes knew what was happening, Apollo shot again, and Bright fell beside his brother. Then, at last, Lightener acted. With all the strength of his powerful arms he lifted his mighty hammer and threw it at the god.

The force of the hammer broke the rim of the mountain under Apollo's feet, and sent it crashing down into the fires below. Apollo would have gone with it, if he had not leaped away just in time. Yet even as he leaped, a thunderbolt crashed against his crown of laurel and tore it from his head. Blue and yellow and white lights flashed inside his head.

Then Apollo felt himself going down. His head was spinning. His feet were slipping on loose rocks. He would surely have fallen into the roaring fires below him, but at the last moment the end of his bow caught in a crack in a stone. With one foot already over the edge, the god was saved.

Slowly he pulled himself up and away from the broken rim of the mountain. As Lightener sent thunderbolt after thunderbolt crashing around him, Apollo pulled his bow out of the crack in the stone. He dared not stand up, for fear of showing himself against the sky. So, on his knees, he took aim as best he could, and shot.

The last of the Cyclopes fell.

People on earth heard the thunder. They saw lightning flashing in a clear blue sky, and were afraid. Zeus on his mountaintop saw it, too. He came to see who was hurling his thunderbolts. When he found the Cyclopes dead, he in his turn was angry. To punish Apollo for what he had done, he sent him to serve as a slave to a mortal for all of a long year.

It was a terrible punishment for a god. To serve a mortal! But Apollo found his master kind and gentle. He was a young king named Admetus, and he was more like a friend to Apollo than a master.

Apollo also found his work pleasant. He spent most of his time on the green banks of a river, caring for his master's cattle and sheep and goats. It was an easy life as well as a pleasant one. He could even look up into the sky above him and watch his own white herds on any windy day. So the time went by.

Near the end of the year, Apollo was able to serve Admetus in another way, a way that was more worthy of a god.

The king of a nearby land had a daughter named Alcestis. She was beautiful and gentle, and Admetus wanted her for his wife. But when he asked her father for her hand, he was told that he must come for her in a chariot pulled by a lion and a wild boar harnessed together. Only such a man would be worthy of her, her father said.

Admetus was sad. What man could harness a lion? Or even a wild boar? And could anyone ever drive the two of them, together? They would tear each other to pieces. No man could do what the king asked.

But a god could, said Apollo! He leaped at the chance to do such a deed.

Apollo set off into the hills at once. There among the rocks he found a roaring lion. Then he went into the woods. There he caught a wild boar with great sharp tusks. And then, with pieces of strong new leather, Apollo harnessed the two animals together.

But it was just as Admetus had feared. The two wild creatures turned on each other, roaring and snarling. The lion tried to tear the boar with his claws. And the boar tried to rip the lion's belly with his terrible tusks. But Apollo stopped them.

He stopped them with his lyre!

The God of Music took his lyre and began to play. At the first sounds of the music the roaring stopped. The lion's anger left him; the boar forgot his wildness. Like two gentle lambs they walked together, following Apollo and his music. So he brought them to Admetus.

Then, in his chariot pulled by a lion and a wild boar, Admetus went to get Alcestis, and he brought her home as his wife.

Apollo had served his master well.

THE BATTLE WITH DEATH

APOLLO'S YEAR as a slave was at its end. Admetus had been a good friend as well as a kind master. Apollo wanted to leave him with promises for a happy future: for good fortune, long life, and many children. So, with his farseeing eyes, Apollo looked to see what the future held for Admetus.

What he saw made his face grow pale and his eyes grow large with horror. In a dark mist Apollo saw a shining thread. Pressed to the thread he saw the blades of great sharp shears. Around the thread he saw in the mist three ugly hags. One of the three held the shears in her bony hand.

The three hags Apollo saw were the three Fates, goddesses of birth and death. One Fate sat spinning the threads of life, forever spinning, a thread for the life of every person born into the world. The second Fate gave colors to the threads, and wove them together, bright and dark, long and short. The third held the fateful shears, and cut each thread when it was no longer needed in the pattern.

These were the hags Apollo saw. The third Fate was at that moment in the act of cutting the thread of Admetus's life.

There was no future for Admetus.

More swiftly than thought, Apollo acted. He went like the wind to where the Fates were and put his hand between the blades of the shears. Then, holding the shining thread in his hand, he begged the Fates for the life of his friend.

"No," they said, "the pattern of life cannot be changed, not even for you, O Apollo. The thread must be cut."

But the god would not give up. And because he was Apollo, at last even the hard hearts of the Fates were moved.

"We will do what we can," they said at last. "A thread must be cut; that much cannot be changed. But we are willing to cut some other thread instead of this one. If Admetus can find someone to die in his place, we will let him live."

Admetus was filled with joy when Apollo told him that his life could be saved. But his joy soon turned to sorrow. None of his subjects was willing to die for him. Not one. They had risked their lives for him many times in battle. But in battle the end was always in doubt. Now, when death was sure, no one would take his place.

Not even his own mother or father.

"But you are old and I am young," he said to them. "You have lived your lives. They have been long, happy ones. My life has just begun. Won't you give your few last years to buy long years of life for me, your own son?"

"No," said his mother in her old cracked voice.

"No," said his father in his weak one. "What right have you to ask us to die for you? The years of life left to us are few, but they are that much more sweet."

Then Admetus went home to his wife and threw himself in her arms. All his life he had been brave. But now, when he knew that he must surely die, fear overcame him. Life was good, he thought, why must he leave it so soon? He was filled with horror at thoughts of that bony specter, Death, and of the world of the dead to which Death would take him.

"Dark, dark, all is dark," he wept.

"Do not fear," said Alcestis. Her sweet voice was like the voice of a mother soothing a frightened child. "Do not fear, my husband. I will go with Death in your place. Let the Fates cut my life's thread instead of yours."

So Admetus's life was saved, but at a terrible cost.

When Alcestis lay, pale and still, waiting for Death, Admetus knew at last what his fears had done. He would have long life, it was true. But what was long life without his loving wife? Admetus cursed himself and his own weakness.

But it was too late. Death stood at his door demanding to be let in. And that is a demand no mortal can deny. Not even Apollo, standing beside the door, could make Death go away without Alcestis.

When Apollo saw that his words could do no good, he turned his thoughts to the one man in all the world who might overcome Death and take Alcestis from him by force. That one was Hercules, the strongest man in all the world.

Now, Hercules was Admetus's friend, too, and he was at that time not far away. So Apollo put it into his mind to come to see his friend Admetus. And he came, not knowing that Alcestis lay dying.

And, like the good friend he was, Admetus welcomed Hercules. He did not even tell him that Alcestis was dying. He wanted his friend to enjoy his visit. But Admetus could not hide all his sadness.

"Why do you welcome me with such sad looks?" asked Hercules. "And why are you wearing black? Is someone dead?"

"A woman of my house is dying," Admetus told him. "Today we must bury her, so I cannot make merry with you as a good friend should. But make yourself at home. You are always welcome here."

Admetus gave Hercules a room far from the sounds of weeping, and sent him food and wine. Hercules ate and drank. Feeling lonely without his friend, he drank more. And then more. Then, to cheer himself up, he began to sing.

The men who were serving him became angry at the noise he made.

"How can you show so little feeling for a friend's sorrow?" they asked. "Our queen is dying, yet you are singing."

"Your queen? Alcestis?" Suddenly Hercules was filled with shame for what he had done. "But Admetus did not tell me!"

"He did not want to make you feel unwelcome."

"Who has ever had such a friend!" said Hercules, and tears filled his eyes.

Then he began to feel black anger — anger, and sorrow, and shame, and a wild need to do something.

"I will show Admetus that I am his friend, too!" he shouted. "Let me find this Death! I'll take his bony neck in my two hands, and never let him go until he gives Alcestis up. Show me where she is."

"No one can overcome Death," the men said. "Not even you, O Hercules. Besides, it is too late. See, the people are coming back from the tomb. Death is already with her."

But Hercules would not be stopped. He pushed the men away and ran to the tomb. There he found the bony specter standing beside Alcestis. The specter's clammy hand was on her hand; his foul breath filled the tomb.

Hercules took the specter by the arms and pulled him away from Alcestis. Then he turned the thing around, and then — ! Then he was frozen with horror as he looked into those two black eyeless holes, and saw those grinning teeth. For a moment he could not move.

It was only a moment, but it was enough for Death to shake himself loose. Then Hercules felt the specter's hands on his own neck. Bony fingers held him in a grip of iron, stopping his breath. The thing's cold clammy skin made his own skin creep. And what strength! Who would have thought the bony thing could have so much strength in him?

Hercules knew that he had met his match.

He took Death in his arms, and squeezed. With all his strength he squeezed that bony body. Back and forth the two of them fought. But the fingers around Hercules's neck would not let go. Hercules was choking.

Death was winning, and he grinned at the thought of taking mighty Hercules back with him to the world of the dead.

With the last of his breath Hercules cried to Apollo for help. With the last of his strength he reached up and took Death's bony hands in his two great meaty ones. In despair he tried to pull those hands away. He squeezed the bony things with all his mighty strength.

Apollo heard his cry. The strength of Hercules's hands did not fail. As a dark mist began to swim before his eyes, Hercules felt bones crack. The fingers around his neck relaxed, at last. Hercules had broken Death's grip.

Gasping for breath, he threw the specter from him. He stood a moment to let the spinning in his head stop. Then he took Alcestis by the hand, and led her out of that foul place.

He led her back to her husband Admetus, his good friend — and Apollo's friend.

When Admetus turned to thank Apollo, he was gone. The year was over. He had served his friend and master as best he could. There was nothing more to keep him.

But Apollo knew he had only put Death off for a time. He knew that, in the end, Death would surely come for his friends. For they were mortal.

Now, at last, Apollo's anger at Zeus was gone. It was true that Zeus had slain his two sons. But Death would have come for them, in the end. For they, too, were mortal. And it was he himself who had made them mortal, by loving mortal women.

With this year on earth Apollo came to know that his place was among the gods, not on earth with mortals. Only once more would he ever play a personal part in the lives of men. That would be in a great war between the Greeks and the Trojans.

But that is another story.

POSTSCRIPT

APOLLO is no longer worshiped as a god. But still men honor his name.

It was for Apollo, God of the Sun, that men named the chariot in which they first dared to go into the far heavens, out beyond the loving hold of mother earth. And it was to the Moon that they went, to Apollo's sister's silver moon. Apollo, Protector of Mankind, sheltered the men on those first flights and brought them safely home.

And it is Apollo who makes the boldest promises for man's future in the distances of space — Apollo, God of Prophecy.

PROPER NAMES

(with guide to pronunciation)

Ad me′ tus
Al ces′ tis
A pol′ lo
A ri′ on
Ar′ tem is
As cle′ pi us
Au tol′ y cus
Clyt′ ie
Cre u′ sa
Cro′ nus
Cy clo′ pes
Daph′ ne
Del′ phi
E′ ros
Her′ cu les
Her′mes
I′ on
Iph′ i tus
Le′ to
Mer′ cu ry
Mi′ das
Or′ pheus
Pan
Pha′ e thon
Py′ thon
Sat′ urn
Ti mo′ lus
Ti′ tans
Zeus